NIGHT LIGHTS OF THE NORTH

Remember to always look skyward at night!

Barbara Parker

By Barbara Parker
Illustrated by Linda Thompson
Photographs by Steve DuBois

P9-CSV-496

NIGHT LIGHTS OF THE NORTH

Text, illustrations and photographs copyright © 2014 by Barbara Parker, Linda Thompson and Steve DuBois. No part of this book may be copied in whole or in part by digital or mechanical means without the permission from the publisher, except in use for education.

ISBN: 978-1-57833-990-7
Library of Congress Control Number: 2014941971

Printed by Everbest Printing Co., Ltd., in Guangzhou, China, through Alaska Print Brokers, Anchorage, Alaska

Design: Vered R Mares, Todd Communications
Illustrations: Linda Thompson
Photographs: Steve DuBois, used by permission

Published by:

Northern Lights Publishing Co.
Box 1035
Delta Junction, Alaska 99737
Phone: 907-895-1032
barb.parker1955@gmail.com

Distributed by:
Todd Communications
611 E. 12th Ave.
Anchorage, Alaska 99501-4603
(907) 274-TODD (8633) • Fax: (907) 929-5550
with other offices in Juneau and Fairbanks, Alaska
sales@toddcom.com • www.alaskabooksandcalendars.com

NIGHT LIGHTS OF THE NORTH

is dedicated to Lynie, Ruth, Elana
and to all those in the north who look skyward at night.

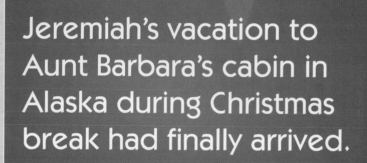

Jeremiah's vacation to Aunt Barbara's cabin in Alaska during Christmas break had finally arrived.

Jeremiah wondered what it would be like to celebrate Christmas in a cabin without electric lights.

Aunt Barbara, a science teacher, would certainly think of something to brighten the holiday season.

Jeremiah had heard about Aunt Barbara's three big husky dogs. Their names were Rory, Boris and Alice.

They made themselves
at home in the cabin.

"Aunt Barbara, why
are your dogs named
Rory, Boris and Alice?"
Jeremiah asked.

"I named Rory, Boris and Alice after the night lights, of course. These lights are called the aurora borealis," Aunt Barbara explained.

"Are they like Christmas lights?"
Jeremiah asked hopefully. [11]

Aunt Barbara had a twinkle in her eye and exclaimed, "Do you want to hear about the best light show?"

Jeremiah wondered how this light show was going to occur without electricity.

He settled down with Rory, Boris and Alice on the couch as Aunt Barbara began…

"The night lights are powered by a wind full of tiny particles blowing from the sun toward Earth."

Magnetic shield

"Earth is protected from the sun's wind by an invisible magnetic shield.

"The wind flows around Earth's magnetic shield, but a few of the particles in the wind do get through the shield and are trapped in Earth's atmosphere near the North and South Poles."

"When the sun's tiny particles enter our atmosphere, they hit larger particles called atoms and molecules 60 to 200 miles above the surface of our Earth."

Nitrogen molecule

Oxygen atom

"Oxygen is one type of atom found in our upper atmosphere, and nitrogen is one type of molecule found in our upper atmosphere."

"The atoms and molecules have little particles circling them called electrons."

Electron

"When the wind from the sun hits these electrons, they get excited and jump up and then fall back down."

"When the electrons fall back down, light is given off."

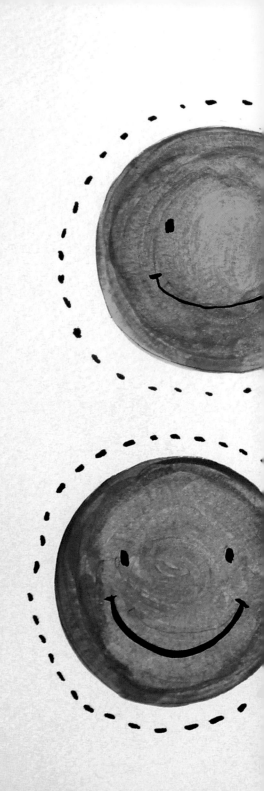

"The oxygen atoms about 200 miles high in our atmosphere give off a red light.

"The oxygen atoms about 60 to 150 miles high in our atmosphere give off a yellow-green light.

"The nitrogen molecules about 60 miles high in our atmosphere give off a purple light."

21

"Maybe the night lights are shining now!" exclaimed Jeremiah with rising excitement.

Rory, Boris and Alice bound for the door sensing a night adventure.

"Let's go back outside and find out…"

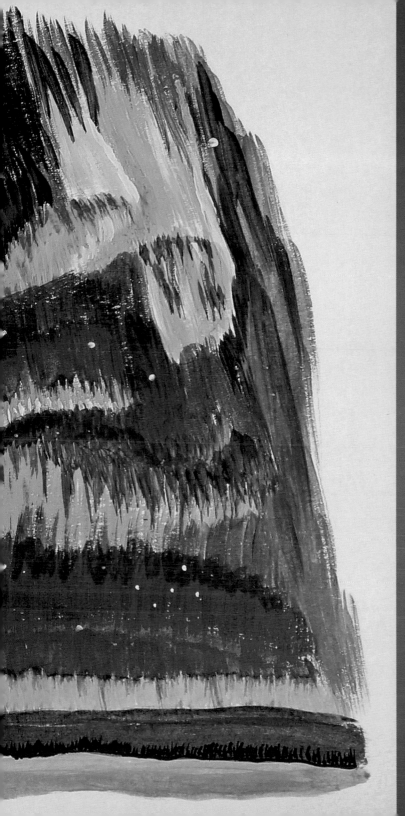

"These are the best Christmas lights ever..." Jeremiah whispered as he gazed up at the aurora borealis, the night lights of the north.

Glossary:

Aurora borealis: Swirls and bands of red, green and purple lights in the sky at night around the North Pole

Particle: A very tiny piece of matter

North Pole: Located at the top of the Earth

South Pole: Located at the bottom of the Earth

Magnetic field: A shield protecting Earth from the solar wind

Solar wind: Tiny particles that travel very fast away from the sun. Some of these particles become trapped in our atmosphere around the North and South Poles of Earth.

Atom: The smallest piece of a pure substance

Molecule: It is made of two or more atoms stuck together.

Oxygen atom: About 60 - 150 miles above the Earth's surface, oxygen atoms create a pale yellow-green light when particles from the solar wind hit them. About 200 miles above the Earth's surface, oxygen atoms create a red light when particles from the solar wind hit them.

Nitrogen molecule: About 60 miles above the Earth's surface, nitrogen molecules create a purple light when particles from the solar wind hit them.

Electron: A tiny piece of electricity that flies around an atom or a molecule

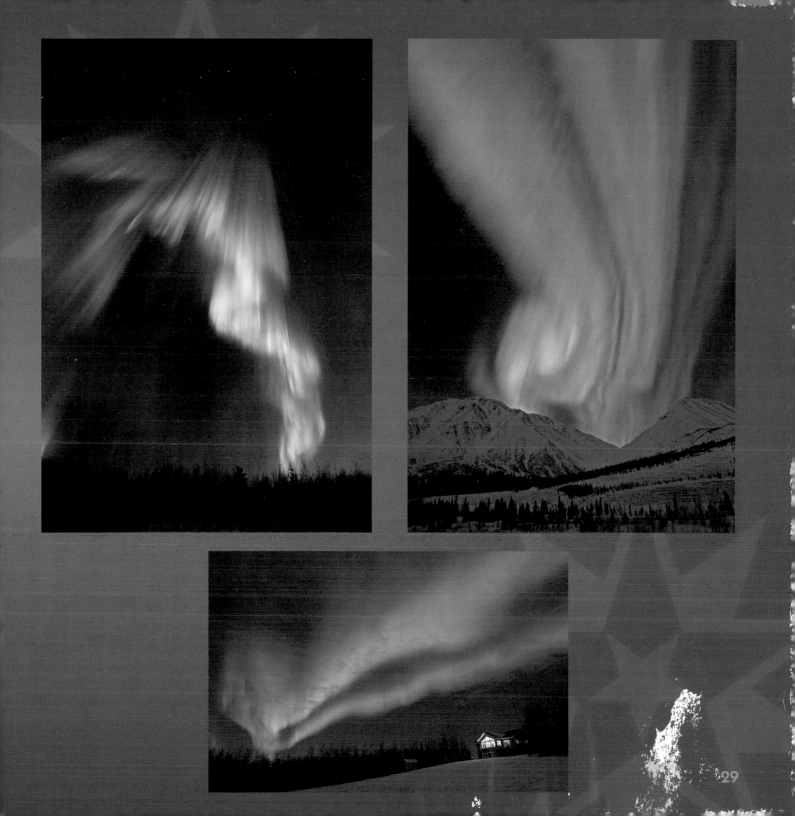

I would like to thank:

Linda Thompson, friend and artist, for so graciously agreeing to illustrate my story,

Steve DuBois, friend and neighbor, for allowing me to include some of his many aurora photographs,

Dr. Neal Brown, Chief Scientist for "Alaska Science Explained", and former director of the Alaska Space Grant Program, for helping me keep my aurora facts accurate,

James Matney, Erica Parker and Cathy Parker, for encouraging me to write this book one hot lazy summer afternoon while we could do nothing but talk on the patio.

Barbara Parker

Linda Thompson   Barbara Parker   Steve DuBois

Linda Thompson, Barbara Parker and Steve DuBois reside in the heart of Alaska in the town of Delta Junction. Barbara Parker is a retired science teacher having taught in the Delta/Greely School District and the Sitka School District. Linda Thompson earned her art degree at Andrews University, Berrien Springs, Michigan. Steve DuBois is a retired wildlife biologist and a professional wildlife and aurora photographer.